Contents

Icons used in this book

This 'pointer' icon marks the brief introduction that sets the piece of writing in context and provides useful background information.

This 'be safe' icon marks important information relating to the use of the text – including personal safety.

This icon indicates that it would be useful for you to have access to a dictionary.

London goes wild

 The World Cup is an international football tournament that has been held once every four years since 1930. This article from the *Observer* newspaper describes the thrill that Londoners felt when England won the World Cup in 1966.

Britain erupted with joy last night after England had won football's World Cup final at Wembley.

Patriotic fervour, unequalled since **VE** day, spread all over the country in celebration of the 4–2 victory over West Germany.

As the team arrived at the Royal Gardens Hotel in Kensington for a banquet, armed linked **cordons** of police popped open like seams when a crowd of over ... mobbed the players. Cries of "England", "Ramsey", "Moore", "Stiles", "Charlton" greeted them on a balcony before the Union Jack-waving crowd.

Traffic in the West End was at a complete standstill. Thousands of cars and pedestrians jostled around Leicester Square, Piccadilly Circus and Trafalgar and Parliament Squares.

Teenagers who had not been at the match clambered into the Trafalgar Square fountains. The pubs were full and cinemas and theatres empty. Groups of people danced and sang in the streets.

An **AA** spokesman said, "It's like **VE** night, election night and New Year's Eve all rolled into one."

★★★   ★★★   ★★★

This was the most dramatic of all World Cup finals, with England scoring twice in extra time after Germany had drawn level in the closing minute and roused the crowd of 93 000 to a frenzy. And it had riveted the attention of nearly 600 million more – one fifth of the world's population – by television and radio.

From the *Observer*, 31 July 1966

Glossary

AA stands for Automobile Association. The AA would have helped to keep the traffic moving in London on the night of the World Cup final.

cordons lines or rings

VE stands for 'Victory in Europe'. It marks the day at the end of World War 2 (1939–45) on which Germany surrendered to the British and to the armies from other countries which had supported them (known as the Allied Forces).

1 The word 'fervour' means (ring **two**):

flavour   enthusiasm   rush   freedom   excitement.

2 marks

2 Name **one** indicator that the crowd was out of control.

_____

1 mark

3 After the match where did the team go to celebrate?

_____

1 mark

4 Which public places were busiest that night? (ring **one**):

cinemas   theatres   pubs   parks

1 mark

5 What figurative expression (metaphor) describes the crowd breaking through the police barricade?

_____

1 mark

6 Give **two** reasons why it was a good idea for the team to go on a balcony to greet their fans.

_____

_____

2 marks

7 Why was the World Cup victory of 1966 compared to VE Day of 1945?

_____

_____

1 mark

8 Roughly how many people were alive in the world in 1966?

_____

1 mark

page 5
total out of 10

How to make a wormery

 The scientist Charles Darwin (1809–1882) believed that without worms, life on earth would be impossible. They make soil richer, encouraging healthy plant growth, and reduce the amount of plant waste in the environment. The instructions here tell you how to breed worms, which you can then release into your garden or local park.

Materials

- 2-litre plastic drinks bottle
- plant pot filled with soil or compost
- black paper, cardboard or material
- crushed chalk – school chalk will do (or pea gravel can be used instead)
- sand
- soil or compost
- dead leaves
- earthworms (see 'How to hunt for worms', below)
- a marker pen

 Always wash your hands after handling soil.

Instructions

1 Cut the top and bottom off the plastic bottle, leaving a tall cylinder.
2 Put about ten earthworms into the soil in the plant pot.
3 Place the cylinder made from the bottle on top of the soil and fill it with alternate layers of soil, sand and crushed chalk or gravel if you are using it. (The sand and chalk or gravel layers need only be thin.)
4 Mark the levels of the layers of soil, sand and chalk/gravel on the cylinder with the marker.
5 Place some dead leaves on top – preferably broken up into smallish pieces.
6 Cover the cylinder with the black paper, cardboard or material to keep out the light.
7 Keep everything damp – not wet – and leave for several days. Lift the cover and observe what has happened.

Notes

There should be roughly 85 per cent soil and 15 per cent other materials in the wormery. The wormery needs to be kept somewhere cool and once set up can be left for one or two weeks. If you leave it any longer than this, the worms are in danger of dying. The worms can be released where they were caught. After another week or so, the wormery can be set up again.

How to hunt for worms

Method 1 – Habitat hunt   Turn over stones and dead wood, look under leaf litter and dig in bare earth.
Method 2 – Stamping up and down   Worms are attracted to the surface by vibrations.
Method 3 – Soaking   Thoroughly wet an area of grass, cover it with black plastic and wait for 30 minutes. The water floods the worms' burrows and unless they come to the surface they will drown.
Method 4 – Twanging   Put a garden fork into an area of grass and rock it backwards and forwards for 15 minutes.

1 Look at the instructions for making a wormery, numbered 1 to 7. What is similar about the first word in each instruction?

_____

2 Some words are in coloured print. What is the reason for this and how does it help the reader?

_____

3 Which material may be used as an alternative to chalk?

_____

4 How do you create a cylinder from a bottle?

_____

5 The wormery's thickest layers will be made of what?

_____

6 What sort of leaves do you need?

_____

7 Why do you think it is necessary to keep out the light?

_____

8 How long can you keep a wormery without any worms dying?

_____

9 Why do you think you should leave it 'another week or so' before setting up another wormery?

_____

10 Which methods of finding worms require no tools or equipment?

_____

11 a) What is the name of the method that involves rocking a garden fork to and fro?

_____

b) How long does this method take? _____

Why?

The Cornish poet Charles Causley was inspired by folk songs, ballads and hymns that he heard as a child. Here he uses a series of questions to describe Susanna's feelings one Bonfire Night (5th November). This date marks the failed attempt in 1605 of a man called Guy Fawkes to blow up the Houses of Parliament. The dummy placed on Bonfire Night fires is still known as a 'guy'.

Why do you turn your head, Susanna,
And why do you swim your eye?
It's only the children on Bellman Street
Calling, *A penny for the guy!*

Why do you look away, Susanna,
As the children wheel him by?
It's only a dummy in an old top-hat
And a fancy jacket and tie.

Why do you take my hand, Susanna,
As the pointing flames jump high?
It's only a bundle of sacking and straw.
Nobody's going to die.

Why is your cheek so pale, Susanna,
As the whizzbangs flash and fly?
It's nothing but a rummage of paper and rag
Strapped to a stick you spy.

Why do you say you hear, Susanna,
The sound of a last, long sigh?
And why do you say it won't leave your head
No matter how hard you try?

Best let me take you home, Susanna.
Best on your bed to lie.
It's only a dummy in an old top-hat.
Nobody's going to die.

Charles Causley (1917–2003)

1 Ring **two** adjectives that might describe how Susanna is feeling.

horrified   bored   upset   surprised   excited   curious

2 marks

2 How did the poem make you feel? Explain why.

_____

_____

2 marks

3 a) How is the dummy dressed?

_____

1 mark

b) What is it stuffed with?

_____

1 mark

4 Give an example suggesting that Susanna has a strong imagination that makes her think a lot about things she observes.

_____

1 mark

5 What exactly are the 'whizzbangs'?

_____

1 mark

6 Name **one** thing that Susanna does that shows she is nervous.

_____

_____

1 mark

7 a) Who do you think might be asking the questions?

_____

1 mark

b) What do they say twice to try and reassure Susanna?

_____

1 mark

8 What does the speaker advise Susanna to do when she gets home?

_____

1 mark

page 9
total out of 12

Dogs are good for you!

 The dogs that we now keep as pets are the descendants of wolves that entered villages in search of food about 12 000 years ago. Later, people began to use dogs to guard, herd and hunt. In the twenty-first century, as this article describes, dogs can bring us other benefits.

Owning a dog is good for your mental and physical health, more so even than cats, researchers claim today.

Dr Deborah Wells, a senior lecturer at the Canine Behaviour Centre of Queens University, Belfast, found that dog owners have lower cholesterol and blood pressure, fewer minor physical ailments, and are less likely to develop serious medical problems.

In a paper published today by the British Psychological Society, she said, "It is possible that dogs can directly promote our well being by buffering us from stress, one of the major risk factors associated with ill health. The ownership of a dog can also lead to increases in physical activity and facilitate the development of social contact, which may enhance both physiological and psychological human health in a more indirect manner."

She found that people who took cats and dogs from animal rescue shelters noticed a decrease in minor ailments such as headaches, colds and dizziness a month after the rescue visit. But only dog owners maintained the improvements ten months later – cat owners did not.

The research, published in the Health Psychology Journal, found that dogs could also act as 'early-warning systems' for more serious illnesses including cancer and epilepsy.

From 'Improve your health, become a dog owner' by Lynne Wallis
Daily Telegraph, 22 January 2007

1 Mental health relates to the mind. Physical health relates to _____.

2 What might happen if a human being is very stressed?

_____

1 mark

3 Name any **two minor** and any **two major** ailments mentioned in this article.

a) minor _____

2 marks

b) major _____

2 marks

4 How might owning a dog increase a person's physical activity **and** widen their social contact?

_____

_____

1 mark

5 Physiological is to the body as psychological is to the _____.

1 mark

6 Facilitate means (ring **one**):

organise   develop   make easier   impede.

1 mark

7 What made researchers believe that dogs are even better than cats at keeping people healthy?

_____

_____

1 mark

8 What advice would this report offer to someone with high blood pressure?

_____

_____

1 mark

9 In what publication could you read the full report?

_____

1 mark

page 11
total out of 12

The 'ration book' Olympics

 During and after World War 2 (1939–45), Britain was short of money. To ensure that the food and clothes available were shared fairly, the amounts each person could have, and when these were used, were written in a 'ration book'. This text describes the arrangements for providing food to visiting athletes during the Olympic Games held in London in 1948, when rationing was still in force.

When London hosted the 1948 Olympic Games despite post-war rationing due to food shortages, it became known as the 'austere' or 'ration book' Olympics. British athletes were used to a restricted diet and food substitutes, such as powdered egg and milk. But the Government feared that limiting visiting athletes' diet might have a 'bad psychological effect' so they fed all athletes Category 'A' meal allowances – the equivalent to those provided for heavy workers (coal miners and dockers) but with the additions of two pints of liquid milk per head per day and half a pound of chocolates and sweets per head per week.

After the Olympic Committee warned visiting nations of the daily ration, many competing nations brought large quantities of food to be used by competitors generally: the Argentines, for example, brought 100 tons of meat, Holland promised fruit and vegetables, and Iceland, frozen mutton.

Supplies of food at one of the Olympic Housing Centres in Uxbridge were said to be 'ample', largely owing to the 'munificence of the US team'. Enriched white flour was flown to the camp daily from Los Angeles. But not all competitors were happy. Many of the Mexican Olympic team bought food in town, as they did not like English cooking.

Despite the warning of food shortages, some teams still complained: the Korean team were dissatisfied with their meat allowance; American teams requested supplies of grapefruit and fresh oranges after they complained of 'stomach trouble'. Requests for poultry caused the Government to state that there would be 'trade and consumer repercussions' if supplies were made to Housing Centres from an already 'extremely short' supply.

Despite the restrictions, the Games were a success, with provisions for all. In a press conference the Minister of Food, John Strachey, stated that the estimated increased consumption by the competitors and officials amounted to 0.16 of 1 per cent, 'a completely insignificant amount'.

Adapted by Celia Warren
from material supplied by the National Archives of Great Britain

1 Look at the root word (shown in **bold**) and complete this sentence with related words.

A person who **competes** is a _____ who takes part in a _____.

2 The word 'austere' means (ring **two**):

sad   severe   hard-going   wartime   extreme.

3 Which phrase suggests that a restricted diet might make athletes feel miserable and unmotivated?

_____

4 Compared with heavy manual workers, visiting athletes were thought to need a diet that was (ring **one**):

smaller   similar   bigger.

5 What food did the Dutch promise to contribute to all competitors?

_____

6 Enriched white flour came from (ring **one**):

Mexico   America   Argentina   Iceland.

7 Which teams wanted more citrus fruit, and why?

_____

_____

8 Who was the Government's Minister for Food in 1948?

_____

9 What is the significance of the milk being referred to as 'liquid milk'?

_____

_____

Robin Hood

Robin Hood was probably a real person who lived in Sherwood Forest, near Nottingham, sometime between 1100 and 1300. People have written stories about him ever since. Many of these celebrate the victory of good over evil. Today, Sherwood Forest Country Park and Visitor Centre attracts several million visitors every year.

Autumn burnished the forest to red gold. Early frosts rimed the grasses and rusted the bracken. The air was sharp and the sky silver blue. In a clearing, some three dozen of Robin's men were practising their skills with the broad-sword. The wine of the bright morning sharpened their senses, sent their blood racing as they thrust and parried, fighting over the carpet of crisp leaves, the crash of their weapons booming through the trees.

Gradually each pair of opponents called a truce and fell back to the edge of the clearing to watch the remaining men, until only one pair was left. One man of the pair was tall and lithe, the other an oak tree in motion – Robin Hood and Little John. Since their first meeting on the plank, the two had crossed swords and staves many times and each knew all the tricks of the other.

They moved, now fast, now slow, giving and receiving blows of such power that they would have dropped any other man to the ground. Little John's blade struck down upon his master's left shoulder, crashing against the chain-mail he was wearing for protection. Robin side-stepped, letting the sword blade slide down his back while, with both hands on the hilt of his sword, he hit Little John a punishing blow beneath his right arm, crashing into the giant's armour.

A cheer rose from the watching men, and the bright-eyed lads, sitting like squirrels in the branches of the trees, could not speak for excitement.

Little John swung his blade in a great circle about himself, whistling the air, but Robin had ducked, twisted round, and come at Little John again, quick-footed as a boy, with a powerful blow to his head with the back of his blade. The blow sent Little John stumbling forward, his foot caught on a root and he crashed to the ground like felled timber.

From *The Adventures of Robin Hood*
Patricia Leitch

1 About how many men were practising their fighting skills? (ring **one**):

12   24   36   48

2 Read these statements and check the text to help you decide whether they are correct. Write either 'True' or 'False' next to each one.

a) It is autumn when these events happen.   _____

b) 'Opponents' means 'friends'.   _____

c) They have laid a carpet in the forest.   _____

d) Some squirrels were watching the men fight.   _____

e) Little John is really not little at all.   _____

f) The men are fighting with broad-swords.   _____

3 marks

3 What does the phrase 'call a truce' mean?

_____

1 mark

4 Choose from the box below the words which are synonyms for the following:

a) 'burnished': _____

1 mark

b) 'rimed': _____

1 mark

c) 'parried': _____

d) 'felled': _____

1 mark

    frosted   chopped down   made to shine   dodged and evaded

1 mark

5 At the end of the last fight Robin Hood hits Little John on his (ring **one**):

left shoulder   back   head   right arm.

1 mark

6 After receiving the blow, what makes Little John fall over?

_____

1 mark

7 What is 'timber'?

_____

1 mark

page 15
total out of 12

The veiled lady

 This playscript features the fictional detective Sherlock Holmes, who was created by the author Arthur Conan Doyle. The Sherlock Holmes stories became so popular that Conan Doyle was able to give up his job as a doctor and become a full-time writer instead.

Setting: A Victorian parlour. A lady dressed in black is sitting by a fire. A veil hides her face.

Enter Sherlock Holmes.

Holmes: Good morning, madam. My name is Sherlock Holmes. (*lady stands and shakes Holmes' hand*) Ha, I'm glad to see Mrs Hudson has had the good sense to light a fire. And you shall have hot coffee, madam. I see that you are shivering.

Lady: It is not the cold which makes me shiver. (*sitting down*)

Holmes: What then?

Lady: It is fear, Mr Holmes. It is terror. (*raising her veil to show a shocked face*)

Holmes: You mustn't be afraid (*patting her arm*). We shall soon set matters right, I have no doubt. You have come by train, I see.

Lady: How do you know?

Holmes: I observe a return ticket tucked inside your glove. You must have started out early. Yet you had a lengthy drive in a dog-cart, along busy roads, before you reached the station.

Lady (*raising her eyebrows*): How …?

Holmes: There is no mystery, madam. The left arm of your coat is spattered with mud in no fewer than seven places. The marks are fresh. Only a dog-cart throws up mud in that particular way. And even then – only if you sit to the left of the driver.

Lady: You are perfectly correct. I left home before six this morning and came in by the first train to Waterloo. Sir, I have no-one to turn to for help. My friend Mrs Farintosh, whom you once helped, gave me your address. Oh, sir, do you think you could help me, too? I hope you may advise me how to walk amid the dangers that surround me.

Holmes: I am all attention, madam. Tell me everything that will help me advise you upon the matter.

Dramatisation by Celia Warren
of a scene from 'The Adventure of the Speckled Band' by Arthur Conan Doyle (1859–1930)

Schofield & Sims **Key Stage 2 Comprehension** Book 2

1 Is the lady shivering with cold or with fear?

_____

2 If you were designing costumes for this play, how would you describe the lady's costume? Include as much detail as possible.

_____

_____

2 marks

3 What makes the lady think that Sherlock Holmes might help her?

_____

1 mark

4 If you were Sherlock Holmes, what reason might you consider for the lady keeping her face hidden on her journey?

_____

1 mark

5 What does Sherlock Holmes say and do to reassure the lady?

_____

_____

2 marks

6 What transport did the lady use before boarding the train? What clue reveals this to Sherlock Holmes?

_____

_____

2 marks

7 What does Holmes say to tell the woman that he is listening carefully?

_____

1 mark

8 Why are some words in brackets?

_____

1 mark

9 In a story a conversation would include tag words, such as 'said' or 'asked'. What punctuation is used here to show that a character is beginning to speak?

_____

1 mark

page 17
total out of 12

Battered by hurricane winds

About once every 100 years, the United Kingdom experiences a major storm. Once in every 200 years or so, the storm is severe. On 16 October 1987, a violent storm hit the south of England. This news report gives some of the main facts about the storm and the damage it caused.

After the most severe night of storms to hit southern England since 1703, 18 people died and more have been injured, mainly by debris from buildings and falling trees. Weeks of steady rain have weakened tree roots, so that trees fell easily. Some buildings had their roofs blown off. A caravan park was razed to the ground and Shanklin Pier on the Isle of Wight was completely destroyed. Two firemen were killed in Dorset, on their way to an emergency call, and five people died in Dover Harbour. Rescue workers struggled to respond to a record number of calls as winds from the west reached up to 110 mph (177 km/h). The winds lashed areas as far apart as Wales, the southern counties of Britain, the Channel Islands and London.

Boat yards and yachts on the south coast were severely damaged. A Sea Link ferry was blown ashore in Folkestone. Southern Britain has now started a huge clear-up operation. Commuters have been advised to stay at home as blocked roads and railway lines will prevent them from getting to work.

It was a few days ago that the Meteorological Office noticed a strengthening depression over the Atlantic and predicted some stormy weather. Normally the South East and East Anglia escape the big storms from the Atlantic. The unexpected path of this storm caught weather reporters off guard. The previous evening, the BBC's weatherman Michael Fish assured viewers, "There's no hurricane coming". The storm, he predicted, would run along the length of the English Channel, safely away from the land. Instead it carved a pathway of destruction right across southern England.

Record numbers of claims

Insurance companies are preparing themselves for record numbers of claims. Since many buildings insurance policies cover damage caused by storms, homeowners have already begun contacting them.

BBC news reports suggest that, in the London Borough of Ealing alone, 600 calls were made by people whose homes and cars had been struck by falling trees, roof tiles, and other items dislodged by the hurricane-force winds. In an interview with the BBC, Len Turner of Ealing Council said that government funding might be required to deal with the repair bills that local councils are facing.

"It's going to take an enormous amount of effort and money; I hope we can look to the Government to support us because the burden on local rate payers is going to be enormous."

Celia Warren

1 What caused most of the injuries on the night of the hurricane?

_____

_____

1 mark

2 Why were trees so easily uprooted?

_____

_____

1 mark

3 From which direction was the hurricane wind blowing? (ring **one**):

north   south   east   west

1 mark

4 In 'clear-up operations', what might need removing, and from where? Give as full an answer as possible.

_____

_____

2 marks

5 To what does the sub-heading refer?

_____

1 mark

6 Where was a pier destroyed?

_____

1 mark

7 Who were local councils going to ask for help with the clear-up costs?

_____

1 mark

8 a) What are 'commuters'?

_____

1 mark

b) Why were they advised to stay at home after the hurricane?

_____

_____

1 mark

The thrill of wartime work

During times of crisis, a government may sometimes try to influence people's behaviour so that they will help the country to overcome its difficulties. Publications that aim to influence people in this way are called 'propaganda'. In World War 2 (1939–45), some novels encouraged people to help the 'war effort'. This extract encourages teenage girls and women to become farm workers by joining the Land Army. So many of the men and boys had gone away to fight in the war that there were not enough of them available for this work.

Motherless Peggy has parted from her father, who is rejoining his ship. She is setting off to join the Land Army.

"'Smile when you wave me goodbye' is a mushy song, but there's something in it," Peggy was thinking. "One up to me. I didn't let him down over parting. My eyes are quite dry. I'm glad he said, 'No waving,' for I simply couldn't have kept a stiff upper lip over seeing her sail. Oh, dear little dirty, rolling *Iris!* God keep you safe and take care of you and guide you past mines and submarines and bombers, and bring you and Daddy safe home again."

Not feeling quite so tough, and seeing the railway approach through a mist of which she was duly ashamed, Peggy repaired to the train. Once settled in the corner of a third-class compartment, her own immediate affairs came bubbling up on top of her excited thoughts, and finally drove out the regrets of parting.

How could she feel unhappy? Her head and her heart were full of thoughts that jostled and raced one another, just as her eager pulses were racing with the rush of life, life that was taking hold of her blithe youth, snatching her up out of the quiet waiting time of schooldays, into the stern, real, workaday world, a world at war.

"It's splendid to be born now," Peggy thought. "People have been born and lived and died, and never once had a chance to do things …"

From *Peggy Speeds the Plough*
Madge S. Smith

1 What is the purpose of propaganda?

_____

_____

1 mark

2 Why would putting propaganda in a story setting help its purpose?

_____

_____

1 mark

3 What slang word does Peggy use that means 'over sentimental'?

_____

1 mark

4 Peggy keeps a 'stiff upper lip'. What does that mean?

_____

1 mark

5 What is the name of the ship on which Peggy's father goes to sea?

_____

1 mark

6 What is the 'mist' of which Peggy is ashamed?

_____

1 mark

7 'Repair' often means 'to mend'. What does it mean here, in the second paragraph?

_____

1 mark

8 What sort of work would Peggy be doing in the Land Army?

_____

1 mark

9 How do you think a farmer might feel when young women arrived to take the place of his regular farm workmen when they went off to fight in the war? What sort of problems would the farmer and the land girls face?

_____

_____

_____

2 marks

Arthur's sister turned to stone

The King Arthur so well known in British legend is first described in Welsh stories of the tenth century. It is this literary character who is associated with the Knights of the Round Table. The legendary Arthur may have been based on a real historical figure who led British troops in the defeat of Saxon invaders in 518.

A strange silence settled over the company of horsemen and their commander. Their bridles ceased to jingle, their stirrups to swing. The horses turned as grey as dusk. The men's beards stiffened, their features set, and their backbones turned, vertebra by vertebra, into columns of pebbles balanced one on another. In short, they turned to stone, their breath to dust, and their outline against the cliff to no more than the fresco carving on a wall. At their head stood the 'statue' of Morgan, her robe grey, her horse grey, her skin and bone grey over grey.

Entering the valley, Arthur's horse slowed to a halt, trembling violently. The King dismounted and ran his fingers over the contours of flank and mane and robe. He stood before the 'carving' of his sister and gazed up at her stony features, beautiful, hard, bloodless, believing all life had gone out of her. Either she had put this terrible end to herself, out of guilt, or else her magic had soured into this paralysing greyness. He laid his hand over hers – a stone hand resting on a stone pommel. Then he turned away, with tears in his eyes. "Mount up, men," he said, "and let's go home."

After he had gone, after the noise of galloping had faded to silence, the rock face shivered. Puffs of dust erupted here and there, and pebbles trickled down. With the slowness of sap returning to a winter tree, Morgan's hand turned from grey to pink then lifted from the pommel of her saddle. She raised it in a triumphant fist. Behind her, the dozen stone horses shook themselves and broke free of the cliff, bridles jingling, nostrils snorting.

From *King Arthur and the Round Table*
Geraldine McCaughrean

1 Which verb indicates the sound made by movement of the horses' bridles?

_____

2 A backbone is made up of a series of small bones. What is each of these called?

_____

3 What is happening that makes the author compare these bones to pebbles?

_____

4 Why are the words 'statue' and 'carving' in quotation marks?

_____

_____

5 In this text, who is it that discovers the petrified riders?

_____

6 The word 'paralysing' means (ring **one**):

the worse for wear   stony   made unable to move   magical.

7 A 'dozen stone horses' means there were (ring **one**):

10   12   20   several.

8 Name **one** of the first signs of life returning to the riders.

_____

9 In the opening paragraph the adjective 'grey' appears five times. What effect does the author achieve by reusing the same word again and again?

_____

_____

10 Name **one** sound mentioned in this passage.

_____

Overheard on a saltmarsh

Harold Monro ran a poetry bookshop in London, and also wrote poems himself. The famous poet Wilfred Owen (1893–1918) lived in a flat above the bookshop and encouraged Harold Monro in his writing. This poem is set in an area of land that is flooded by sea water at high tide.

Nymph, nymph, what are your beads?

Green glass, goblin. Why do you stare at them?

Give them me.
    No.

Give them me. Give them me.
    No.

Then I will howl all night in the reeds,
Lie in the mud and howl for them.

Goblin, why do you love them so?

They are better than stars or water,
Better than voices of winds that sing,
Better than any man's fair daughter,
Your green glass beads on a silver ring.

Hush, I stole them out of the moon.

Give me your beads, I want them.
    No.

I will howl in the deep lagoon
For your green glass beads, I love them so.
Give them me. Give them.
    No.

Harold Monro (1879–1932)

1 This poem is a conversation between a nymph and who else?

_____

2 What is the special name given to the place where this conversation takes place?

_____

3 Who is the first to speak?

_____

4 What does the goblin want?

_____

5 What are the nymph's beads made of?

_____

6 What holds the beads together?

_____

7 Why does the nymph say 'Hush' when asked where the beads come from?

_____

8 What does the goblin say he will do in several different places if he doesn't get what he wants?

_____

9 What **two** questions does the nymph ask the goblin?

_____

_____

The arrival of a rugged seaman

 Robert Louis Stevenson was a Scottish novelist, poet and travel writer. In his novel *Treasure Island* the main character, Jim Hawkins, describes his search for the treasure buried by a wicked pirate, Captain Flint. This extract is taken from the beginning of the story. Jim remembers the arrival of a rugged seaman, who came to lodge at his father's inn ...

I remember him as if it were yesterday, as he came plodding to the inn door, his sea-chest following behind him in a hand-barrow – a tall, strong, heavy, nut-brown man, his tarry pigtail falling over the shoulder of his soiled blue coat, his hands ragged and scarred, with black, broken nails, and the **sabre** cut across one cheek, a dirty, livid white. I remember him looking round the cover and whistling to himself as he did so, and then breaking out in that old sea-song that he sang so often afterwards:

"Fifteen men on the dead man's chest – Yo-ho-ho, and a bottle of rum!"

in the high, old tottering voice that seemed to have been tuned and broken at the **capstan** bars. Then he rapped on the door with a bit of stick like a **handspike** that he carried, and when my father appeared, called roughly for a glass of rum. This, when it was brought to him, he drank slowly, like a **connoisseur**, lingering on the taste and still looking about him at the cliffs and up at our signboard.

"This is a handy cove," says he at length; "and a pleasant sittyated grog-shop. Much company, mate?"

My father told him no, very little company, the more was the pity.

"Well, then," said he, "this is the berth for me. Here you, matey," he cried to the man who trundled the barrow: "bring up alongside and help up my chest. I'll stay here a bit," he continued. "I'm a plain man; rum and bacon and eggs is what I want, and that head up there for to watch ships off. What you mought call me? You mought call me captain. Oh, I see what you're at – there," and he threw down three or four gold pieces on the threshold. "You can tell me when I've worked through that," says he, looking as fierce as a commander.

From *Treasure Island*
Robert Louis Stevenson (1850–1894)

Glossary

capstan a revolving barrel, used to raise or lower a ship's sails
connoisseur an expert who has wide knowledge or experience of a particular thing; a judge of quality
handspike a wooden pole or rod used as a lever, usually on board a ship
sabre a soldier's sword with a curved blade

Schofield & Sims **Key Stage 2 Comprehension** Book 2

1 Give **two** examples from the description of the seaman's appearance that suggest he had lived a rough life.

_____

_____ 2 marks

2 The seaman's voice seemed to have been 'tuned and broken at the capstan bars'. What does that suggest about the age of the man when he first went to sea?

_____

_____ 1 mark

3 Some words spoken by the seaman are spelt strangely. What do these words mean?

a) 'sittyated': _____ 1 mark

b) 'mought': _____ 1 mark

4 Why do you think the author spelt 'sittyated' and 'mought' the way he did?

_____

_____ 1 mark

5 What does the seaman refer to as a 'grog-shop'?

_____ 1 mark

6 In the last paragraph, what **two** things does the landlord want to know about the seaman?

_____

_____ 2 marks

7 What does the seaman want to eat and drink?

_____ 1 mark

The scarecrow

Walter de la Mare wrote short stories, novels and poetry for both adults and children. He especially enjoyed writing for children. Here he writes about the dummy that is made to look like a man and then put up in a field to scare birds away from the crops.

All winter through I bow my head
  Beneath the driving rain;
The North Wind powders me with snow
  And blows me black again;
At midnight in a maze of stars
  I flame with glittering rime,
And stand, above the stubble, stiff
  As mail at morning-prime.
But when that child, called Spring, and all
  His host of children, come,
Scattering their buds and dew upon
  These acres of my home,
Some rapture in my rags awakes;
  I lift void eyes and scan
The skies for crows, those ravening foes,
  Of my strange master, Man.
I watch him striding lank behind
  His clashing team, and know
Soon will the wheat swish body high
  Where once lay sterile snow;
Soon shall I gaze across a sea
  Of sun-begotten grain,
Which my unflinching watch hath sealed
  For harvest once again.

Walter de la Mare (1873–1956)

1 Whose head is bowing?

_____

2 The poem begins in which season?

_____

3 What sort of grain does the scarecrow say will grow when the snow has gone?

_____

4 What are 'those ravening foes'?

_____

5 The 'clashing team' is (ring **one**):

horses pulling a plough   men fighting   crows screeching.

6 What does 'sun-begotten' mean?

_____

7 📖 Use a dictionary to find the meaning of the following words:

a) rime: _____

b) rapture: _____

c) void: _____

8 Quote an example of alliteration from this poem.

_____

Holy horrors

This article is taken from a magazine. It is called 'Holy horrors' because gargoyles, which are the subject of the article, are often found on the outside of church buildings. Notice how the article speaks to you directly, and then holds your interest with many interesting facts.

Walk around any town and you'll probably find a gargoyle, clinging to the edge of a building, gazing outwards over the skyline. The origins of these bizarre bits of plumbing, for that is what they first were, remain obscure. They can be traced back to ancient Egypt, Greece and Rome when waterspouts depicting lions, eagles and other creatures were common. The word 'gargoyle' comes from the old French *gargouille* (throat) – from which our verb 'to gargle' also derives.

Each carved gargoyle has its own personality and, coming in so many guises, they are hard to **decipher**. Some, it seems, were intended to ward off evil spirits. Those at **Notre-Dame** in Paris are said to keep watch for drowning victims in the Seine, coming alive at night and flying to the rescue. Other gargoyles appear frozen in flight, as those at Beverley Minster. Tortured-looking gargoyles could have been intended to warn **medieval** people against evil. At York Minster a gargoyle howls with his head in his hands, as if in hell.

Gargoyles using their hands to pull their mouths open, known as 'mouth-pullers', are seen by some as **embodiments** of Satan. Others believe that – far from symbolising the devil – these are just funny representations of childish mouth-pulling games. Certain gargoyles actually display the physical characteristics of the devil, including wings, vampiric **fangs** and clawed feet, as can be seen in a vivid example at Lichfield Cathedral. A gargoyle with a human face surrounded by leaves depicts the 'Green Man', a **pagan** symbol of **fertility**, while a few gargoyles represent real people.

From their origins thousands of years ago to the present day, gargoyles have held our attention. We still smile at their appearance and wonder at their meaning. So, next time you're on a day out – look up. You might find you're being watched.

Glossary
decipher make out the meaning of
embodiments forms or bodies that represent a character
fangs long sharp teeth used for piercing
fertility fruitfulness of living things
medieval relating to the Middle Ages (the eleventh to fifteenth centuries)
Notre-Dame ancient cathedral in Paris
pagan following ancient beliefs

Abridged from the article of the same title by Oliver Garnett and Claire Masset
National Trust Magazine, Autumn 2007

1 Which word suggests that gargoyles form part of roof drainage and gutters?

_____ 1 mark

2 What other purpose are they supposed to have?

_____ 1 mark

3 The word 'obscure' means (ring **one**):

original   not easily understood   strange   ancient. 1 mark

4 Which verb, meaning 'to wash your throat' comes from the same root as the word 'gargoyle'?

_____ 1 mark

5 How are some gargoyles made to look extra funny?

_____ 1 mark

6 What features make some gargoyles look like the devil?

_____ 1 mark

7 The word 'vampiric' means like a _____. 1 mark

8 a) What mythical character do gargoyles sometimes represent?

_____ 1 mark

b) What appears around his face?

_____ 1 mark

9 Whereabouts on a building would you be most likely to see a gargoyle?

_____ 1 mark

page 31
total out of **10**

De

Thomas Hood (1799–1845) wrote a famous poem called 'No!'. In 'No!' he described all the things that he missed during the month of November – for example, the sun, warmth and butterflies. This poem by Valerie Bloom is a parody: she uses a similar idea but focuses instead on the month of December.

De snow, de sleet, de lack o' heat,
De wishy-washy sunlight,
De lip turn blue, de cold, 'ACHOO!'
De runny nose, de frostbite.
De creakin' knee, de misery,
De joint dem all rheumatic,
De icy bed (de blanket dead)
De burs' pipe in de attic.
De window a-shake, de glass near break,
De wind dat cut like razor,
De wonderin' why you never buy
De window from dat double-glazer.
De heavy coat zip to de throat,
De nose an' ears all pinky,
De weepin' sky, de clothes can't dry,
De day dem long an' inky.
De icy road, de heavy load,
De las' minute Christmus shoppin',
De cuss an' fret 'cause you feget
De ribbon an' de wrappin'.
De mud, de grime, de slush, de slime,
De place gloomy since November,
De sinkin' heart, is jus' de start o' de wintertime,
December.

Valerie Bloom

1 Valerie Bloom was born in Jamaica. Some of the words in her poem are written as they might be said by someone with a Jamaican accent.

a) What word is written as 'de' at the start of almost every line? _____

1 mark

b) Write 'De joint dem all rheumatic' in standard English.

_____

1 mark

2 Why would this poem not work at all if it were written without this accent?

_____

1 mark

3 Does the speaker like the winter? (Write **two** phrases to support your answer.)

_____

_____

2 marks

4 The word 'ACHOO' sounds like a sneeze. It is (ring **one**):

alliterative   onomatopoeic   lyrical   elliptic.

1 mark

5 Why does the speaker describe the blanket as being 'dead'?

_____

1 mark

6 What simile describes the feeling of the icy wind?

_____

1 mark

7 What is happening to make the speaker describe the sky as 'weepin'?

_____

1 mark

8 In the past, the speaker decided not to do something that might have made her house warmer in winter. What is it that she now wishes she had done?

_____

1 mark

9 a) The poem was inspired by Thomas Hood's poem, 'No!'. What is the last line of 'No!'?

_____

1 mark

b) Even if you had never read the poem 'No!', how could you guess its last line?

_____

1 mark

page 33
total out of 12

Alice meets the Cheshire cat

 Lewis Carroll (whose real name was Charles Dodgson) wrote the story *Alice's Adventures in Wonderland* for the children of a friend. It was first published in 1865, and he later wrote other stories for children, including *Through the Looking-glass*.

The door led straight into a large kitchen, which was full of smoke from one end to the other. The Duchess was sitting on a three-legged stool in the middle, nursing a baby. The cook was leaning over the fire, stirring a large cauldron that seemed to be full of soup.

"There's certainly too much pepper in that soup!" Alice said to herself, between sneezes.

There was certainly too much of it in the air. Even the Duchess sneezed occasionally. As for the baby, it was sneezing and howling alternately without a moment's pause. The only things in the kitchen that did not sneeze were the cook and a large cat, which was sitting on the hearth and grinning from ear to ear.

"Please would you tell me why your cat grins like that?" asked Alice. She spoke a little timidly, for she was not quite sure whether it was good manners for her to speak first.

"It's a Cheshire cat," said the Duchess, "and that's why. Pig!"

The Duchess said the last word with such sudden violence that Alice quite jumped. Then she saw that the word was addressed to the baby and not to her. So she took courage, and went on again:

"I didn't know that Cheshire cats always grinned. In fact, I didn't know that cats could grin."

"They all can," said the Duchess, "and most of 'em do."

"I don't know of any that do," Alice said very politely. She felt quite pleased to have got into a conversation.

"You don't know much," said the Duchess, "and that's a fact."

Abridged from *Alice's Adventures in Wonderland*
Lewis Carroll (1832–1898)

1 What tells us that Alice has only just entered the kitchen?

_____

2 How many people are sneezing?

_____

1 mark

3 They are sneezing because of (ring **one**):

the smoke   an allergy to the Cheshire cat   pepper in the air.

1 mark

4 The baby is sneezing and howling alternately. What does 'alternately' mean?

_____

1 mark

5 What container holds the soup?

_____

1 mark

6 How is it heated?

_____

1 mark

7 Who does the duchess call 'pig'?

_____

1 mark

8 What does to 'get into a conversation' mean?

_____

1 mark

9 The word 'timidly' means _____.

1 mark

10 The Cheshire cat is sitting 'on the hearth'. What is a hearth, and why do you think the cat was sitting there?

_____

_____

2 marks

11 Which words explain that the Cheshire cat had a wide grin?

_____

1 mark

page 35
total out of 12

The fox repaid in his own coin

 This story is adapted from the famous poem *The Canterbury Tales*. A group of people going to visit Canterbury Cathedral meet at an inn in London at the start of their journey. To pass time along the way, they decide that each person should tell a story. This is the story told by one of the priests.

In a poor widow's yard lived a fine cockerel, named Chanticleer. One night he awoke terrified. He told his mate, Pertelot, his dream of a hound that threatened him. Dame Pertelot laughed. Chanticleer's dream, she said, was caused by indigestion.

While Chanticleer enumerated other dreams that had come true, he looked on Dame Pertelot's face, and took courage. By dawn, Chanticleer was strutting around as fierce as a lion.

Some days later, as he was proudly crowing at the sun, he spied a fox hiding in a herb bed. Remembering his dream, Chanticleer wanted to flee, but the fox said, "Gentle sir, don't be afraid. I am your friend. I only came to hear your sweet voice. Your father came to my house once. I never heard anyone but you sing as well as he did. Let me hear you imitate your father."

Chanticleer, flattered by the sly fox's remarks, stretched his neck, closed his eyes, and began to crow loudly. The fox, jumping up, seized him by the throat, and fled towards the woods. Dame Pertelot made such a racket that the widow ran from her cottage. She called the neighbours, who helped chase the fox. But as Chanticleer lay helpless in the fox's grip he made a plan.

"Dear sir," said he to his captor, "if I were you, I would turn on those proud people and tell them that you're keeping this cockerel, and will eat him, whatever they do."

"Indeed," declared the fox, "I shall."

But, as he spoke, the cockerel slipped from his mouth and quickly flew out of reach.

"Oh alas," said the fox, "I'm sorry I scared you. I mean no harm. Gentle sir, come down again, and let me explain."

But Chanticleer replied that he had been deceived once and would not be deceived again. And so the fox was paid in his own coin – flattery.

Story based on 'The nun's priest's tale' from *The Canterbury Tales*
Geoffrey Chaucer (1343–1400)
retold in the *Children's Encyclopaedia* by Arthur Mee

1 If Chanticleer is a cockerel, what sort of bird is his mate, Dame Pertelot?

_____

1 mark

2 What made the cockerel remember his dream a few days later?

_____

1 mark

3 Why did he think it might come true?

_____

1 mark

4 📖 Use a dictionary to find the meaning of the word 'enumerated'. Write the meaning on the line.

_____

1 mark

5 The cause of Chanticleer's bad dream, according to Pertelot, was (ring **one**):

poverty   fear   indigestion   pride.

1 mark

6 Why do you think the fox is described as 'sly'?

_____

1 mark

7 Find words in the story that have the same meaning as the following words:

a) saw, spotted: _____

1 mark

b) noise: _____

1 mark

c) tricked: _____

1 mark

8 Write the simile that describes how Chanticleer walks.

_____

1 mark

9 Who was the cockerel's captor?

_____

1 mark

10 If someone repays you in your own coin, what does it mean? (ring **one**):

a) they flatter you

b) they behave towards you just as you behaved towards them

c) they give you your money back.

1 mark

Digging

Edward Thomas started his writing career as a journalist and biographer. In 1914, at the start of World War 1, he met the American poet Robert Frost, who encouraged him to write poetry. The following year, Thomas joined the army and in 1917 he was killed in battle.

To-day I think
Only with scents, – scents dead leaves yield
And bracken, and wild carrot's seed,
And the square mustard field;

Odours that rise
When the spade wounds the root of tree,
Rose, currant, raspberry, or **goutweed**,
Rhubarb or celery;

The smoke's smell, too,
Flowing from where a bonfire burns
The dead, the waste, the dangerous,
And all to sweetness turns.

It is enough
To smell, to crumble the dark earth,
While the robin sings over again
Sad songs of Autumn mirth.

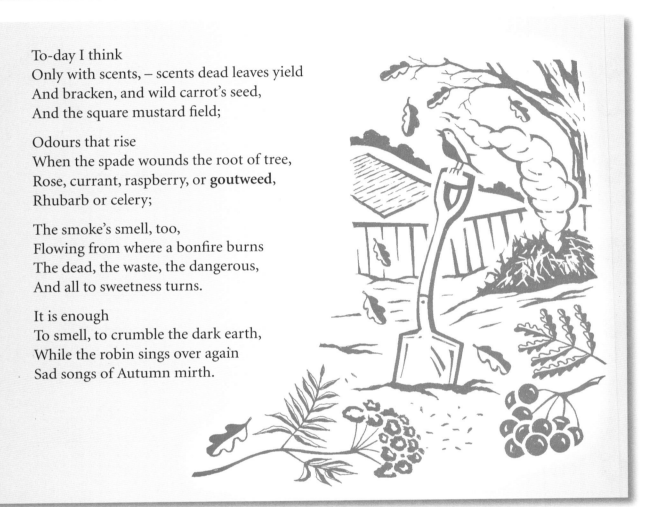

Edward Thomas (1878–1917)

Glossary

goutweed a low plant with strong roots that spreads quickly over the ground

1 The words 'scents' and 'sense' are homophones. What does that term mean?

_____

1 mark

2 What does the poet mean by 'Today I think only with scents'?

_____

1 mark

3 Which other **two** words meaning 'scent' does the poet use?

_____

_____

2 marks

4 The verb 'yield' means (ring **one**):

to give up   to fall apart   to die.

1 mark

5 Which verb describes cutting into tree roots?

_____

1 mark

6 Which smell is the result neither of nature nor of digging?

_____

1 mark

7 Why is it unusual for the word 'flowing' to be used with 'the smell of smoke'?

_____

1 mark

8 The word 'mirth' means _____. (📖 Use a dictionary to check.)

1 mark

9 Most of this poem focuses on the sense of smell. What other sense is referred to at the end of the poem?

_____

1 mark

10 a) Why is 'mirth' an odd word to follow 'sad songs'?

1 mark

_____

b) What does it tell us about the digger's mood?

1 mark

_____

page 39
total out of 12

Book 2
total out of 200

Schofield&Sims

Comprehension skills are essential to literacy. Without them, even the most fluent readers will struggle to read for meaning.

Key Stage 2 Comprehension provides a unique collection of stimulating texts that appeal strongly to both boys and girls, together with questions that build and stretch comprehension skills and widen vocabulary. Comprising four one-per-child activity books, the series is designed for seven to 11 year olds to use in school or at home and is also suitable for some older children and young people; you can give varying levels of support according to the needs of each child. Providing more than 72 texts in total, each with questions on the facing page, the series encourages readers both to pay close attention to literal meaning and to make inferences and deductions. Readers are also given intensive practice in observing how different kinds of writing are structured and in identifying literary devices and their effects.

The Key Stage 2 Comprehension activity books are easy to use and mark and provide a permanent record of each child's work, helping you to monitor progress. When the child has completed all the activities in the book, you can divide by two the total marks gained to obtain a percentage score.

Key Stage 2 Comprehension Book 2 is for children whose reading skills are fluent and accurate. It includes:

- excellent examples of broadsheet journalism, such as a description of the celebrations following England's victory in the 1966 World Cup

- an instructional text, 'How to make a wormery', that children will love

- enthralling extracts from classic fiction – *The Adventures of Robin Hood*, *Treasure Island* and *Alice's Adventures in Wonderland* – plus stories based on the *Canterbury Tales* and Arthurian legend

- an intriguing playscript adapted from a Sherlock Holmes detective story

- thought-provoking poetry from Charles Causley, Walter de la Mare, Valerie Bloom and Edward Thomas.

The separate **Teacher's Guide** gives you all you need to use **Key Stage 2 Comprehension** to its full potential. The teaching notes for each text include an introduction, answers and a wealth of further activities, including at least one speaking and listening task. Other useful features include cross-curricular content charts and photocopiable group record sheets.

The full range of books in the series is as follows.

Key Stage 2 Comprehension Book 1	ISBN 978 07217 1154 6
Key Stage 2 Comprehension Book 2	ISBN 978 07217 1155 3
Key Stage 2 Comprehension Book 3	ISBN 978 07217 1156 0
Key Stage 2 Comprehension Book 4	ISBN 978 07217 1157 7
Key Stage 2 Comprehension Teacher's Guide	ISBN 978 07217 1158 4

ISBN 978-07217-1155-3

9 781721 711553

MIX
Paper from responsible sources
FSC® C010219

ISBN 978 07217 1155 3
Key Stage 2
Age range 7–11 years
£2.95 (Retail price)